How Guinness Found His Family

a memoir

This story is dedicated to my grandsons: Graham, Miles, Reid, and Evan, and to all the animals that have found forever homes from shelters throughout the United States.

Thanks to my early readers who gave me their thoughts, suggestions, and words of encouragement on this project. They include: Nancy, Mary Jo, Carol, Brownell, Karen, Anne and Merry, Carolyn and Jack, and my family.

Proceeds from the sale of this book will be given to Colorado Animal Rescue (CARE) and the No Barriers Fund at Colorado Mountain College.

www.caringbooks.org

How Guinness Found His Family

a memoir

written by **Kathleen Barger**

illustrated by **Jade MEyer**

Kathy Barger

Hi, my name is Guinness! I am fifteen years old and am one lucky cat. This is a story of a holiday miracle, and it happened to me.

Would you like to hear my story? It is a story about my journey from Minnesota to Indiana to Colorado and on to New Hampshire. I have traveled a lot of miles around the United States.

Minneapolis, Minnesota is where my tale begins. It's a nice city with lots of lakes and biking and walking paths. Winter in Minnesota is very cold and snowy.

Fortunately, I have been an indoor cat, because I like to keep warm and cozy.

In my early life, I was lost and living on the streets of the big city. It was scary, and I was all alone. Each day I walked around to search for bits of food, dodging stray dogs and strangers. Lucky for me, someone saw me and took me to an animal shelter. Animal shelters help lost or abandoned animals find forever homes.

A nice, young couple adopted me and took me home.

I felt special.

They named me Guinness. I roamed around the house, and chattered a lot to let them know how happy I was. Lucky for me, I got to sleep on my new parents' big, comfy bed.

I love an adventure. I stuffed myself into a brown box on the kitchen floor! I thought it was funny, because my human mom was walking around and calling GUINNESS! all over the house. She was surprised when I peeked out of the box! She was so happy to find me that she gave me a treat of catnip.

Another morning, I jumped up and sat at my dad's computer and watched all the action. Words and pictures on the screen were moving and hopping around. There were dinging sounds when the words changed. It's boring watching technology. I prefer bird feeders.

Oh boy. Next we got a dog named Griffin. Griffin chased me all over the house. I knew he was only playing, but I had to be alert all day! He went to doggie behavior training school, but it didn't do much good.

Three human baby boys joined our family in five years; our house had lots of toys all over the place. Sometimes baby gates were put up to keep Griffin out of the rooms. Griffin couldn't get over the gates, but I could.

I jumped the gates whenever I wanted to get away from Griffin. Yay! Always have an escape route.

I loved to watch the little boys play with all kinds of toys – Legos, building blocks, puzzles and they cooked as pretend chefs in a toy kitchen.

After a few years, my mom and dad decided not to live together, so I moved to Indiana with my mom, the boys and Griffin. My dad went to live in Colorado. I was so sad. Where was I going? Would I feel safe in my new place? I knew I would miss my dad. I didn't understand.

We had fun most of the time in our new home, but once one of the boys sprayed WD-40 oil on my fur! Yikes! WD-40 is used for lots of things – rids kids' swings of squeaky noises, removes crayons from walls, and keeps flies off cows.

NOT FOR CAT FUR! I hated baths; after that mess, I needed one to clean my coat. Actually, the warm water felt good, and I didn't get sick licking off the oil. I know all of us were upset at the changes in our family, and we had to learn to trust again.

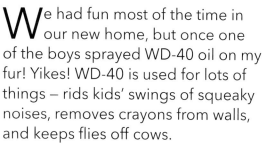

Then I went to live with my dad in Colorado. Colorado is a beautiful place with lots of mountains. I lived near a big, big mountain called Mt. Sopris. I loved Colorado.

Probably the reason I have lived so many years is that I am an indoor cat. It keeps me safe from all the wild creatures in the outdoors. It's dangerous out there, and I don't need to roam outside to be happy.

Dad and I took care of each other. I loved getting all the attention and having a quiet home. Once again, I learned to trust my human dad.

Then my dad moved back to Indiana to be near the family. He could not take me to his new house. I was very sad. Have you ever felt this way? He told me he would find me a good home.

Dad had a buddy, Mr. Gordon, who agreed to take me and give me a home with him and his dog, Fido. Well, Fido was faithful to Dad's friend, but not very nice to me. He chased me through the house, and I became very stressed and unhappy. The tip of my tail twitched almost non-stop with all this confusion.

Since I was stressed living there, my dad's friend, Mr. Gordon, took me to CARE (Colorado Animal Rescue), the local animal shelter. CARE knew that with my complete medical records and such a great name like Guinness, I would certainly find a new loving home. I wasn't so sure.

I don't blame anyone for all the changes. Everyone had tried to do his or her best for me, but still I was lonely and scared. There were times when I would curl up in a ball and dream of a new home and a family petting me gently. I would play with my paws to ease my scary thoughts. All of us find ways to cope with strong feelings and need someone to notice when we are having a difficult time.

Now, this is where the holiday miracle comes in. The shelter put an advertisement in the local paper's Pet Section to help me find a home. I didn't know it, but the grandparents of the three little boys saw my photo and the ad in the paper. And guess what? They were MY grandparents, too!

They spend much of the winter in Colorado; enjoy skiing and the beauty of the Roaring Fork Valley. The other months they are in New Hampshire by a beautiful lake. What luck for me!

Their dog, Schatzie, was a rescue from a New Hampshire shelter, so she was used to cats. And to make things even luckier, she had met me before!

Schatzie and I had a trial meeting at CARE, and she behaved. She didn't chase me. She sniffed me, which wasn't too much fun, but then she went into the corner of the room and took a nap. Can you imagine my good fortune?

So, I became the luckiest cat on planet Earth. I was going to be with my family once again and forever!

Soon, the little boys will be here for a ski vacation, and I am so excited to be able to see them again.

Thanks to all the people who helped me reunite with my family. I am grateful for all the loving care, and especially to the CARE shelter for placing that ad.

Sometimes there are happy endings. Shelters everywhere help animals find a new family or, like me, return to a former one. I will live out my cat life with my family – I may be old but I am one lucky cat.

Wisdom from Guinness on Adopting a Forever Friend

Human Friends,

If you would like to adopt a shelter pet, here's some advice from a cat that has had amazing luck with adoptions. Consider these things:

What kind of pet will be a good addition to your family? If you live in a large city, perhaps a small dog or cat will be better for your house or apartment. If you have plenty of room, large dogs will be happy with you! Or don't forget about a cat like ME! I don't need much room, just some good windows to imagine I am out prowling around in the world. Also, I love a scratching post and high places to spy on my family.

Where can I find information to help me make a decision? Talk to local shelters and visit your library. Bookstores can also help you decide how to choose a good pet for you and your family. Shelters are the BEST, but of course, I am very partial and grateful to the ones that helped me.

A new Forever Friend is a commitment. Forever Friends need lots of love, care and attention. You know that from reading about ME. First, make your house and yard safe. I am a cat that pukes after I eat a houseplant, so we don't have plants at our house. (Or, you can plant a "kitty garden" with edible plants like catnip.) Sometimes I accidentally knocked breakables off low bookcases or tables, so make sure you put valuables up higher. If you are planning to have your cat or dog go outside, make sure the fence does not have holes. Even better are "toppers" or "catios" for cats to prevent escaping over a fence. New pets like to explore and are curious. You would be so sad if your Forever Friend got out.

Fostering a cat is a great way to try out the responsibility of pet ownership. Foster care can help an animal become comfortable in a home instead of a cage, and a happy animal is much more adoptable. Plus, an animal can help a child, too, and can teach responsibility, compassion and empathy.

Talk with your family and decide:

Who will take care of your Forever Friend? Or your Foster Friend?

Will you need to make any special arrangements such as doggy day care? Pet sitters? Who will play with them and give them exercise?

If there are small children in your family, make sure they know how to handle us. Thankfully, no one picked me up by my TAIL – but you never know!

Do you have a veterinarian ready to take on a new family member? The vet will become one of your BEST FRIENDS!

List of needs for your new friend:

Proper food
Water
Bed
Litter box
Toys (interactive toys, and cuddle toys)

Scratching post
Grooming tools
Collar for ID
Microchip for identity
Harness and leash for walking

About the Author

Kathleen Barger resides in Carbondale, Colorado. This true story about Guinness is her first book. She taught school many years ago and believes in the joy of having animals find their Forever Human Friends!

About the Illustrator

Jade Meyer is in the 7th grade at Waldorf School on the Roaring Fork in Carbondale. Jade's love is the arts. When not singing, dancing or performing in a theatre production, Jade can be found with pencil and paper doing her next favorite passion, drawing/art.